THIS BUCKET LIST BELONGS TO

. . . .

THE
BUCKETLIST

1 .... ☐
2 .... ☐
3 .... ☐
4 .... ☐
5 .... ☐
6 .... ☐
7 .... ☐
8 .... ☐
9 .... ☐
10 .... ☐
11 .... ☐
12 .... ☐
13 .... ☐
14 .... ☐
15 .... ☐
16 .... ☐
17 .... ☐
18 .... ☐
19 .... ☐
20 .... ☐

THE
BUCKETLIST

21 .... ☐
22 .... ☐
23 .... ☐
24 .... ☐
25 .... ☐
26 .... ☐
27 .... ☐
28 .... ☐
29 .... ☐
30 .... ☐
31 .... ☐
32 .... ☐
33 .... ☐
34 .... ☐
35 .... ☐
36 .... ☐
37 .... ☐
38 .... ☐
39 .... ☐
40 .... ☐

BUCKETLIST

41 .... ☐
42 .... ☐
43 .... ☐
44 .... ☐
45 .... ☐
46 .... ☐
47 .... ☐
48 .... ☐
49 .... ☐
50 .... ☐
51 .... ☐
52 .... ☐
53 .... ☐
54 .... ☐
55 .... ☐
56 .... ☐
57 .... ☐
58 .... ☐
59 .... ☐
60 .... ☐

THE
BUCKETLIST

61 .... ☐
62 .... ☐
63 .... ☐
64 .... ☐
65 .... ☐
66 .... ☐
67 .... ☐
68 .... ☐
69 .... ☐
70 .... ☐
71 .... ☐
72 .... ☐
73 .... ☐
74 .... ☐
75 .... ☐
76 .... ☐
77 .... ☐
78 .... ☐
79 .... ☐
80 .... ☐

THE
BUCKETLIST

81 .... ☐
82 .... ☐
83 .... ☐
84 .... ☐
85 .... ☐
86 .... ☐
87 .... ☐
88 .... ☐
89 .... ☐
90 .... ☐
91 .... ☐
92 .... ☐
93 .... ☐
94 .... ☐
95 .... ☐
96 .... ☐
97 .... ☐
98 .... ☐
99 .... ☐
100 .... ☐

~ 1 ~

....

I WANT TO DO THIS BECAUSE

....

TO MAKE THIS HAPPEN I NEED

....

DATE COMPLETED ....

WHERE ....

SOLO – WITH ....

THE STORY

....

....

THE BEST PART

....

....

WHAT I LEARNED FROM THIS

....

....

WOULD I DO IT AGAIN? ....

2

I WANT TO DO THIS BECAUSE
....

TO MAKE THIS HAPPEN I NEED
....

DATE COMPLETED ....

WHERE ....

SOLO – WITH ....

THE STORY
....
....

THE BEST PART
....
....

WHAT I LEARNED FROM THIS
....
....

WOULD I DO IT AGAIN? ....

I WANT TO DO THIS BECAUSE

....

TO MAKE THIS HAPPEN I NEED

....

DATE COMPLETED ....

WHERE ....

SOLO – WITH ....

THE STORY

....

....

THE BEST PART

....

....

WHAT I LEARNED FROM THIS

....

....

WOULD I DO IT AGAIN? ....

4

I WANT TO DO THIS BECAUSE

....

TO MAKE THIS HAPPEN I NEED

....

DATE COMPLETED ....

WHERE ....

SOLO - WITH ....

THE STORY

....

....

THE BEST PART

....

....

WHAT I LEARNED FROM THIS

....

....

WOULD I DO IT AGAIN? ....

5

I WANT TO DO THIS BECAUSE

TO MAKE THIS HAPPEN I NEED

DATE COMPLETED

WHERE

SOLO – WITH

THE STORY

THE BEST PART

WHAT I LEARNED FROM THIS

WOULD I DO IT AGAIN?

I WANT TO DO THIS BECAUSE

....

TO MAKE THIS HAPPEN I NEED

....

DATE COMPLETED ....

WHERE ....

SOLO – WITH ....

THE STORY

....

....

THE BEST PART

....

....

WHAT I LEARNED FROM THIS

....

....

WOULD I DO IT AGAIN? ....

7

....

I WANT TO DO THIS BECAUSE

....

TO MAKE THIS HAPPEN I NEED

....

DATE COMPLETED ....

WHERE ....

SOLO – WITH ....

THE STORY

....

....

THE BEST PART

....

....

WHAT I LEARNED FROM THIS

....

....

WOULD I DO IT AGAIN? ....

8

I WANT TO DO THIS BECAUSE

TO MAKE THIS HAPPEN I NEED

DATE COMPLETED

WHERE

SOLO - WITH

THE STORY

THE BEST PART

WHAT I LEARNED FROM THIS

WOULD I DO IT AGAIN?

9

....

I WANT TO DO THIS BECAUSE

....

TO MAKE THIS HAPPEN I NEED

....

DATE COMPLETED ....

WHERE ....

SOLO – WITH ....

THE STORY

....

....

THE BEST PART

....

....

WHAT I LEARNED FROM THIS

....

....

WOULD I DO IT AGAIN? ....

∾ 10 ∾

I WANT TO DO THIS BECAUSE

TO MAKE THIS HAPPEN I NEED

DATE COMPLETED

WHERE

SOLO – WITH

THE STORY

THE BEST PART

WHAT I LEARNED FROM THIS

WOULD I DO IT AGAIN?

❧11❧

I WANT TO DO THIS BECAUSE

....

TO MAKE THIS HAPPEN I NEED

....

DATE COMPLETED ....

WHERE ....

SOLO – WITH ....

THE STORY

....

....

THE BEST PART

....

....

WHAT I LEARNED FROM THIS

....

....

WOULD I DO IT AGAIN? ....

~12~

I WANT TO DO THIS BECAUSE

....

....

TO MAKE THIS HAPPEN I NEED

....

DATE COMPLETED ....

WHERE ....

SOLO – WITH ....

THE STORY

....

....

THE BEST PART

....

....

WHAT I LEARNED FROM THIS

....

....

WOULD I DO IT AGAIN? ....

❧ 13 ❧

. . . .

I WANT TO DO THIS BECAUSE

. . . .

TO MAKE THIS HAPPEN I NEED

. . . .

DATE COMPLETED . . . .

WHERE . . . .

SOLO – WITH . . . .

THE STORY

. . . .

. . . .

THE BEST PART

. . . .

. . . .

WHAT I LEARNED FROM THIS

. . . .

. . . .

WOULD I DO IT AGAIN? . . . .

∂ 14 ∂

I WANT TO DO THIS BECAUSE

TO MAKE THIS HAPPEN I NEED

DATE COMPLETED

WHERE

SOLO – WITH

THE STORY

THE BEST PART

WHAT I LEARNED FROM THIS

WOULD I DO IT AGAIN?

❧ 15 ❧

I WANT TO DO THIS BECAUSE

TO MAKE THIS HAPPEN I NEED

DATE COMPLETED

WHERE

SOLO – WITH

THE STORY

THE BEST PART

WHAT I LEARNED FROM THIS

WOULD I DO IT AGAIN?

❦ 16 ❦

I WANT TO DO THIS BECAUSE

....

TO MAKE THIS HAPPEN I NEED

....

DATE COMPLETED ....

WHERE ....

SOLO – WITH ....

THE STORY

....

....

THE BEST PART

....

....

WHAT I LEARNED FROM THIS

....

....

WOULD I DO IT AGAIN? ....

❧ 17 ❧

I WANT TO DO THIS BECAUSE

....

TO MAKE THIS HAPPEN I NEED

....

DATE COMPLETED   ....

WHERE ....

SOLO – WITH   ....

THE STORY

....

....

THE BEST PART

....

....

WHAT I LEARNED FROM THIS

....

....

WOULD I DO IT AGAIN?   ....

❧18❧

....

I WANT TO DO THIS BECAUSE

....

TO MAKE THIS HAPPEN I NEED

....

DATE COMPLETED ....

WHERE ....

SOLO – WITH ....

THE STORY

....

....

THE BEST PART

....

....

WHAT I LEARNED FROM THIS

....

....

WOULD I DO IT AGAIN? ....

❧ 19 ❧

I WANT TO DO THIS BECAUSE

TO MAKE THIS HAPPEN I NEED

DATE COMPLETED

WHERE

SOLO – WITH

THE STORY

THE BEST PART

WHAT I LEARNED FROM THIS

WOULD I DO IT AGAIN?

❧ 20 ❧

I WANT TO DO THIS BECAUSE

....

TO MAKE THIS HAPPEN I NEED

....

DATE COMPLETED ....

WHERE ....

SOLO – WITH ....

THE STORY

....

....

THE BEST PART

....

....

WHAT I LEARNED FROM THIS

....

....

WOULD I DO IT AGAIN? ....

⚡21⚡

....

I WANT TO DO THIS BECAUSE

....

TO MAKE THIS HAPPEN I NEED

....

DATE COMPLETED ....

WHERE ....

SOLO – WITH ....

THE STORY

....

....

THE BEST PART

....

....

WHAT I LEARNED FROM THIS

....

....

WOULD I DO IT AGAIN? ....

❧ 22 ❧

I WANT TO DO THIS BECAUSE

....

TO MAKE THIS HAPPEN I NEED

....

DATE COMPLETED ....

WHERE ....

SOLO – WITH ....

THE STORY

....

....

THE BEST PART

....

....

WHAT I LEARNED FROM THIS

....

....

WOULD I DO IT AGAIN? ....

23

....

I WANT TO DO THIS BECAUSE

....

TO MAKE THIS HAPPEN I NEED

....

DATE COMPLETED ....

WHERE ....

SOLO – WITH ....

THE STORY

....

....

THE BEST PART

....

....

WHAT I LEARNED FROM THIS

....

....

WOULD I DO IT AGAIN? ....

24

I WANT TO DO THIS BECAUSE

....

TO MAKE THIS HAPPEN I NEED

....

DATE COMPLETED ....

WHERE ....

SOLO – WITH ....

THE STORY

....

....

THE BEST PART

....

....

WHAT I LEARNED FROM THIS

....

....

WOULD I DO IT AGAIN? ....

❧25❧

. . . .

I WANT TO DO THIS BECAUSE

. . . .

TO MAKE THIS HAPPEN I NEED

. . . .

DATE COMPLETED . . . .

WHERE . . . .

SOLO – WITH . . . .

THE STORY

. . . .

. . . .

THE BEST PART

. . . .

. . . .

WHAT I LEARNED FROM THIS

. . . .

. . . .

WOULD I DO IT AGAIN? . . . .

❧26❧

I WANT TO DO THIS BECAUSE

TO MAKE THIS HAPPEN I NEED

DATE COMPLETED

WHERE

SOLO – WITH

THE STORY

THE BEST PART

WHAT I LEARNED FROM THIS

WOULD I DO IT AGAIN?

❧27❧

I WANT TO DO THIS BECAUSE

....

TO MAKE THIS HAPPEN I NEED

....

DATE COMPLETED ....

WHERE ....

SOLO – WITH ....

THE STORY

....

....

THE BEST PART

....

....

WHAT I LEARNED FROM THIS

....

....

WOULD I DO IT AGAIN? ....

28

I WANT TO DO THIS BECAUSE

....

TO MAKE THIS HAPPEN I NEED

....

DATE COMPLETED ....

WHERE ....

SOLO – WITH ....

THE STORY

....

....

THE BEST PART

....

....

WHAT I LEARNED FROM THIS

....

....

WOULD I DO IT AGAIN? ....

❧ 29 ❧

I WANT TO DO THIS BECAUSE

TO MAKE THIS HAPPEN I NEED

DATE COMPLETED

WHERE

SOLO – WITH

THE STORY

THE BEST PART

WHAT I LEARNED FROM THIS

WOULD I DO IT AGAIN?

❧ 30 ❧

I WANT TO DO THIS BECAUSE

....

TO MAKE THIS HAPPEN I NEED

....

DATE COMPLETED ....

WHERE ....

SOLO – WITH ....

THE STORY

....

....

THE BEST PART

....

....

WHAT I LEARNED FROM THIS

....

....

WOULD I DO IT AGAIN? ....

∽31∾

....

I WANT TO DO THIS BECAUSE

....

TO MAKE THIS HAPPEN I NEED

....

DATE COMPLETED ....

WHERE ....

SOLO – WITH ....

THE STORY

....

....

THE BEST PART

....

....

WHAT I LEARNED FROM THIS

....

....

WOULD I DO IT AGAIN? ....

~32~

I WANT TO DO THIS BECAUSE

....

TO MAKE THIS HAPPEN I NEED

....

DATE COMPLETED ....

WHERE ....

SOLO – WITH ....

THE STORY

....

....

THE BEST PART

....

....

WHAT I LEARNED FROM THIS

....

....

WOULD I DO IT AGAIN? ....

∾33∾

....

I WANT TO DO THIS BECAUSE

....

TO MAKE THIS HAPPEN I NEED

....

DATE COMPLETED ....

WHERE ....

SOLO – WITH ....

THE STORY

....

....

THE BEST PART

....

....

WHAT I LEARNED FROM THIS

....

....

WOULD I DO IT AGAIN? ....

❧34❧

I WANT TO DO THIS BECAUSE
....

TO MAKE THIS HAPPEN I NEED
....

DATE COMPLETED ....

WHERE ....

SOLO – WITH ....

THE STORY
....
....

THE BEST PART
....
....

WHAT I LEARNED FROM THIS
....
....

WOULD I DO IT AGAIN? ....

❧35❧

I WANT TO DO THIS BECAUSE

TO MAKE THIS HAPPEN I NEED

DATE COMPLETED

WHERE

SOLO – WITH

THE STORY

THE BEST PART

WHAT I LEARNED FROM THIS

WOULD I DO IT AGAIN?

36

I WANT TO DO THIS BECAUSE

....

TO MAKE THIS HAPPEN I NEED

....

DATE COMPLETED ....

WHERE ....

SOLO – WITH ....

THE STORY

....

....

THE BEST PART

....

....

WHAT I LEARNED FROM THIS

....

....

WOULD I DO IT AGAIN? ....

❧37❧

I WANT TO DO THIS BECAUSE

TO MAKE THIS HAPPEN I NEED

DATE COMPLETED

WHERE

SOLO – WITH

THE STORY

THE BEST PART

WHAT I LEARNED FROM THIS

WOULD I DO IT AGAIN?

38

I WANT TO DO THIS BECAUSE

....

TO MAKE THIS HAPPEN I NEED

....

DATE COMPLETED ....

WHERE ....

SOLO – WITH ....

THE STORY

....

....

THE BEST PART

....

....

WHAT I LEARNED FROM THIS

....

....

WOULD I DO IT AGAIN? ....

~39~

I WANT TO DO THIS BECAUSE

TO MAKE THIS HAPPEN I NEED

DATE COMPLETED

WHERE

SOLO – WITH

THE STORY

THE BEST PART

WHAT I LEARNED FROM THIS

WOULD I DO IT AGAIN?

❧40❧

....

I WANT TO DO THIS BECAUSE

....

TO MAKE THIS HAPPEN I NEED

....

DATE COMPLETED ....

WHERE ....

SOLO – WITH ....

THE STORY

....

....

THE BEST PART

....

....

WHAT I LEARNED FROM THIS

....

....

WOULD I DO IT AGAIN? ....

❧41❧

I WANT TO DO THIS BECAUSE

....

TO MAKE THIS HAPPEN I NEED

....

DATE COMPLETED ....

WHERE ....

SOLO – WITH ....

THE STORY

....

....

THE BEST PART

....

....

WHAT I LEARNED FROM THIS

....

....

WOULD I DO IT AGAIN? ....

❧42❧

....

I WANT TO DO THIS BECAUSE

....

TO MAKE THIS HAPPEN I NEED

....

DATE COMPLETED ....

WHERE ....

SOLO – WITH ....

THE STORY

....

....

THE BEST PART

....

....

WHAT I LEARNED FROM THIS

....

....

WOULD I DO IT AGAIN? ....

❧43❧

I WANT TO DO THIS BECAUSE

TO MAKE THIS HAPPEN I NEED

DATE COMPLETED

WHERE

SOLO – WITH

THE STORY

THE BEST PART

WHAT I LEARNED FROM THIS

WOULD I DO IT AGAIN?

~44~

I WANT TO DO THIS BECAUSE

TO MAKE THIS HAPPEN I NEED

DATE COMPLETED

WHERE

SOLO – WITH

THE STORY

THE BEST PART

WHAT I LEARNED FROM THIS

WOULD I DO IT AGAIN?

～45～

I WANT TO DO THIS BECAUSE

TO MAKE THIS HAPPEN I NEED

DATE COMPLETED ....

WHERE ....

SOLO – WITH ....

THE STORY

THE BEST PART

WHAT I LEARNED FROM THIS

WOULD I DO IT AGAIN? ....

❧46❧

....

I WANT TO DO THIS BECAUSE

....

TO MAKE THIS HAPPEN I NEED

....

DATE COMPLETED ....

WHERE ....

SOLO – WITH ....

THE STORY

....

....

THE BEST PART

....

....

WHAT I LEARNED FROM THIS

....

....

WOULD I DO IT AGAIN? ....

❧47❧

I WANT TO DO THIS BECAUSE

TO MAKE THIS HAPPEN I NEED

DATE COMPLETED

WHERE

SOLO – WITH

THE STORY

THE BEST PART

WHAT I LEARNED FROM THIS

WOULD I DO IT AGAIN?

❧48❧

I WANT TO DO THIS BECAUSE

....

TO MAKE THIS HAPPEN I NEED

....

DATE COMPLETED ....

WHERE ....

SOLO – WITH ....

THE STORY

....

....

THE BEST PART

....

....

WHAT I LEARNED FROM THIS

....

....

WOULD I DO IT AGAIN? ....

❧49❧

....

I WANT TO DO THIS BECAUSE

....

TO MAKE THIS HAPPEN I NEED

....

DATE COMPLETED ....

WHERE ....

SOLO – WITH ....

THE STORY

....

....

THE BEST PART

....

....

WHAT I LEARNED FROM THIS

....

....

WOULD I DO IT AGAIN? ....

∾50∾

I WANT TO DO THIS BECAUSE

TO MAKE THIS HAPPEN I NEED

DATE COMPLETED

WHERE

SOLO - WITH

THE STORY

THE BEST PART

WHAT I LEARNED FROM THIS

WOULD I DO IT AGAIN?

❧51❧

I WANT TO DO THIS BECAUSE

TO MAKE THIS HAPPEN I NEED

DATE COMPLETED

WHERE

SOLO – WITH

THE STORY

THE BEST PART

WHAT I LEARNED FROM THIS

WOULD I DO IT AGAIN?

~52~

....

I WANT TO DO THIS BECAUSE

....

TO MAKE THIS HAPPEN I NEED

....

DATE COMPLETED ....

WHERE ....

SOLO – WITH ....

THE STORY

....

....

THE BEST PART

....

....

WHAT I LEARNED FROM THIS

....

....

WOULD I DO IT AGAIN? ....

53

I WANT TO DO THIS BECAUSE

TO MAKE THIS HAPPEN I NEED

DATE COMPLETED

WHERE

SOLO - WITH

THE STORY

THE BEST PART

WHAT I LEARNED FROM THIS

WOULD I DO IT AGAIN?

❧54❧

I WANT TO DO THIS BECAUSE

TO MAKE THIS HAPPEN I NEED

DATE COMPLETED

WHERE

SOLO – WITH

THE STORY

THE BEST PART

WHAT I LEARNED FROM THIS

WOULD I DO IT AGAIN?

~55~

....

I WANT TO DO THIS BECAUSE

....

TO MAKE THIS HAPPEN I NEED

....

DATE COMPLETED ....

WHERE ....

SOLO – WITH ....

THE STORY

....

....

THE BEST PART

....

....

WHAT I LEARNED FROM THIS

....

....

WOULD I DO IT AGAIN? ....

∾56∾

....

I WANT TO DO THIS BECAUSE

....

TO MAKE THIS HAPPEN I NEED

....

DATE COMPLETED ....

WHERE ....

SOLO – WITH ....

THE STORY

....

....

THE BEST PART

....

....

WHAT I LEARNED FROM THIS

....

....

WOULD I DO IT AGAIN? ....

∂57∂

I WANT TO DO THIS BECAUSE

TO MAKE THIS HAPPEN I NEED

DATE COMPLETED

WHERE

SOLO – WITH

THE STORY

THE BEST PART

WHAT I LEARNED FROM THIS

WOULD I DO IT AGAIN?

~58~

....

I WANT TO DO THIS BECAUSE

....

TO MAKE THIS HAPPEN I NEED

....

DATE COMPLETED ....

WHERE ....

SOLO – WITH ....

THE STORY

....

....

THE BEST PART

....

....

WHAT I LEARNED FROM THIS

....

....

WOULD I DO IT AGAIN? ....

59

I WANT TO DO THIS BECAUSE

....

TO MAKE THIS HAPPEN I NEED

....

DATE COMPLETED ....

WHERE ....

SOLO – WITH ....

THE STORY

....

....

THE BEST PART

....

....

WHAT I LEARNED FROM THIS

....

....

WOULD I DO IT AGAIN? ....

~60~

I WANT TO DO THIS BECAUSE

....

TO MAKE THIS HAPPEN I NEED

....

DATE COMPLETED ....

WHERE ....

SOLO – WITH ....

THE STORY

....

....

THE BEST PART

....

....

WHAT I LEARNED FROM THIS

....

....

WOULD I DO IT AGAIN? ....

⋙61⋘

I WANT TO DO THIS BECAUSE

TO MAKE THIS HAPPEN I NEED

DATE COMPLETED

WHERE

SOLO – WITH

THE STORY

THE BEST PART

WHAT I LEARNED FROM THIS

WOULD I DO IT AGAIN?

❧62❧

....

I WANT TO DO THIS BECAUSE

....

TO MAKE THIS HAPPEN I NEED

....

DATE COMPLETED ....

WHERE ....

SOLO – WITH ....

THE STORY

....

....

THE BEST PART

....

....

WHAT I LEARNED FROM THIS

....

....

WOULD I DO IT AGAIN? ....

ᴽ63ᴽ

I WANT TO DO THIS BECAUSE

TO MAKE THIS HAPPEN I NEED

DATE COMPLETED

WHERE

SOLO – WITH

THE STORY

THE BEST PART

WHAT I LEARNED FROM THIS

WOULD I DO IT AGAIN?

☙ 64 ☙

....

I WANT TO DO THIS BECAUSE

....

TO MAKE THIS HAPPEN I NEED

....

DATE COMPLETED ....

WHERE ....

SOLO – WITH ....

THE STORY

....

....

THE BEST PART

....

....

WHAT I LEARNED FROM THIS

....

....

WOULD I DO IT AGAIN? ....

❧65❧

I WANT TO DO THIS BECAUSE

TO MAKE THIS HAPPEN I NEED

DATE COMPLETED

WHERE

SOLO – WITH

THE STORY

THE BEST PART

WHAT I LEARNED FROM THIS

WOULD I DO IT AGAIN?

✧66✧

I WANT TO DO THIS BECAUSE

TO MAKE THIS HAPPEN I NEED

DATE COMPLETED

WHERE

SOLO - WITH

THE STORY

THE BEST PART

WHAT I LEARNED FROM THIS

WOULD I DO IT AGAIN?

❦67❧

I WANT TO DO THIS BECAUSE

....

TO MAKE THIS HAPPEN I NEED

....

DATE COMPLETED ....

WHERE ....

SOLO – WITH ....

THE STORY

....

....

THE BEST PART

....

....

WHAT I LEARNED FROM THIS

....

....

WOULD I DO IT AGAIN? ....

~68~

I WANT TO DO THIS BECAUSE

TO MAKE THIS HAPPEN I NEED

DATE COMPLETED

WHERE

SOLO – WITH

THE STORY

THE BEST PART

WHAT I LEARNED FROM THIS

WOULD I DO IT AGAIN?

69

I WANT TO DO THIS BECAUSE

TO MAKE THIS HAPPEN I NEED

DATE COMPLETED

WHERE

SOLO – WITH

THE STORY

THE BEST PART

WHAT I LEARNED FROM THIS

WOULD I DO IT AGAIN?

❧ 70 ❧

I WANT TO DO THIS BECAUSE

TO MAKE THIS HAPPEN I NEED

DATE COMPLETED

WHERE

SOLO – WITH

THE STORY

THE BEST PART

WHAT I LEARNED FROM THIS

WOULD I DO IT AGAIN?

⤜71⤛

....

I WANT TO DO THIS BECAUSE

....

TO MAKE THIS HAPPEN I NEED

....

DATE COMPLETED ....

WHERE ....

SOLO – WITH ....

THE STORY

....

....

THE BEST PART

....

....

WHAT I LEARNED FROM THIS

....

....

WOULD I DO IT AGAIN? ....

~72~

....

I WANT TO DO THIS BECAUSE

....

TO MAKE THIS HAPPEN I NEED

....

DATE COMPLETED ....

WHERE ....

SOLO – WITH ....

THE STORY

....

....

THE BEST PART

....

....

WHAT I LEARNED FROM THIS

....

....

WOULD I DO IT AGAIN? ....

∽73∽

I WANT TO DO THIS BECAUSE

TO MAKE THIS HAPPEN I NEED

DATE COMPLETED

WHERE

SOLO – WITH

THE STORY

THE BEST PART

WHAT I LEARNED FROM THIS

WOULD I DO IT AGAIN?

⤾74⤿

I WANT TO DO THIS BECAUSE

TO MAKE THIS HAPPEN I NEED

DATE COMPLETED

WHERE

SOLO – WITH

THE STORY

THE BEST PART

WHAT I LEARNED FROM THIS

WOULD I DO IT AGAIN?

❧ 75 ❧

I WANT TO DO THIS BECAUSE

TO MAKE THIS HAPPEN I NEED

DATE COMPLETED

WHERE

SOLO – WITH

THE STORY

THE BEST PART

WHAT I LEARNED FROM THIS

WOULD I DO IT AGAIN?

~76~

I WANT TO DO THIS BECAUSE

....

TO MAKE THIS HAPPEN I NEED

....

DATE COMPLETED ....

WHERE ....

SOLO – WITH ....

THE STORY

....

....

THE BEST PART

....

....

WHAT I LEARNED FROM THIS

....

....

WOULD I DO IT AGAIN? ....

❧77❧

I WANT TO DO THIS BECAUSE

TO MAKE THIS HAPPEN I NEED

DATE COMPLETED

WHERE

SOLO – WITH

THE STORY

THE BEST PART

WHAT I LEARNED FROM THIS

WOULD I DO IT AGAIN?

78

I WANT TO DO THIS BECAUSE

TO MAKE THIS HAPPEN I NEED

DATE COMPLETED

WHERE

SOLO – WITH

THE STORY

THE BEST PART

WHAT I LEARNED FROM THIS

WOULD I DO IT AGAIN?

❧79❧

I WANT TO DO THIS BECAUSE

TO MAKE THIS HAPPEN I NEED

DATE COMPLETED

WHERE

SOLO – WITH

THE STORY

THE BEST PART

WHAT I LEARNED FROM THIS

WOULD I DO IT AGAIN?

❧80❧

. . . .

I WANT TO DO THIS BECAUSE

. . . .

TO MAKE THIS HAPPEN I NEED

. . . .

DATE COMPLETED . . . .

WHERE . . . .

SOLO – WITH . . . .

THE STORY

. . . .

. . . .

THE BEST PART

. . . .

. . . .

WHAT I LEARNED FROM THIS

. . . .

. . . .

WOULD I DO IT AGAIN? . . . .

∞81∞

I WANT TO DO THIS BECAUSE
. . . .

TO MAKE THIS HAPPEN I NEED
. . . .

DATE COMPLETED . . . .

WHERE . . . .

SOLO – WITH . . . .

THE STORY
. . . .

. . . .

THE BEST PART
. . . .

. . . .

WHAT I LEARNED FROM THIS
. . . .

. . . .

WOULD I DO IT AGAIN? . . . .

~82~

I WANT TO DO THIS BECAUSE

TO MAKE THIS HAPPEN I NEED

DATE COMPLETED

WHERE

SOLO – WITH

THE STORY

THE BEST PART

WHAT I LEARNED FROM THIS

WOULD I DO IT AGAIN?

❧83❧

I WANT TO DO THIS BECAUSE

TO MAKE THIS HAPPEN I NEED

DATE COMPLETED

WHERE

SOLO – WITH

THE STORY

THE BEST PART

WHAT I LEARNED FROM THIS

WOULD I DO IT AGAIN?

∞84∞

I WANT TO DO THIS BECAUSE

. . . .

TO MAKE THIS HAPPEN I NEED

. . . .

DATE COMPLETED . . . .

WHERE . . . .

SOLO – WITH . . . .

THE STORY

. . . .

. . . .

THE BEST PART

. . . .

. . . .

WHAT I LEARNED FROM THIS

. . . .

. . . .

WOULD I DO IT AGAIN? . . . .

❧85❧

....

I WANT TO DO THIS BECAUSE

....

TO MAKE THIS HAPPEN I NEED

....

DATE COMPLETED   ....

WHERE   ....

SOLO – WITH   ....

THE STORY

....

....

THE BEST PART

....

....

WHAT I LEARNED FROM THIS

....

....

WOULD I DO IT AGAIN?   ....

86

I WANT TO DO THIS BECAUSE

TO MAKE THIS HAPPEN I NEED

DATE COMPLETED

WHERE

SOLO – WITH

THE STORY

THE BEST PART

WHAT I LEARNED FROM THIS

WOULD I DO IT AGAIN?

❧87❧

I WANT TO DO THIS BECAUSE

TO MAKE THIS HAPPEN I NEED

DATE COMPLETED

WHERE

SOLO – WITH

THE STORY

THE BEST PART

WHAT I LEARNED FROM THIS

WOULD I DO IT AGAIN?

~❧ 88 ❧~

I WANT TO DO THIS BECAUSE

....

TO MAKE THIS HAPPEN I NEED

....

DATE COMPLETED ....

WHERE ....

SOLO – WITH ....

THE STORY

....

....

THE BEST PART

....

....

WHAT I LEARNED FROM THIS

....

....

WOULD I DO IT AGAIN? ....

❧89❧

....

I WANT TO DO THIS BECAUSE

....

TO MAKE THIS HAPPEN I NEED

....

DATE COMPLETED ....

WHERE ....

SOLO – WITH ....

THE STORY

....

....

THE BEST PART

....

....

WHAT I LEARNED FROM THIS

....

....

WOULD I DO IT AGAIN? ....

I WANT TO DO THIS BECAUSE

....

TO MAKE THIS HAPPEN I NEED

....

DATE COMPLETED ....

WHERE ....

SOLO – WITH ....

THE STORY

....

....

THE BEST PART

....

....

WHAT I LEARNED FROM THIS

....

....

WOULD I DO IT AGAIN? ....

∂91∂

....

I WANT TO DO THIS BECAUSE

....

TO MAKE THIS HAPPEN I NEED

....

DATE COMPLETED ....

WHERE ....

SOLO – WITH ....

THE STORY

....

....

THE BEST PART

....

....

WHAT I LEARNED FROM THIS

....

....

WOULD I DO IT AGAIN? ....

❧92❧

....

I WANT TO DO THIS BECAUSE

....

TO MAKE THIS HAPPEN I NEED

....

DATE COMPLETED ....

WHERE ....

SOLO – WITH ....

THE STORY

....

....

THE BEST PART

....

....

WHAT I LEARNED FROM THIS

....

....

WOULD I DO IT AGAIN? ....

❧93❧

I WANT TO DO THIS BECAUSE

TO MAKE THIS HAPPEN I NEED

DATE COMPLETED

WHERE

SOLO – WITH

THE STORY

THE BEST PART

WHAT I LEARNED FROM THIS

WOULD I DO IT AGAIN?

94

I WANT TO DO THIS BECAUSE

....

TO MAKE THIS HAPPEN I NEED

....

DATE COMPLETED ....

WHERE ....

SOLO – WITH ....

THE STORY

....

....

THE BEST PART

....

....

WHAT I LEARNED FROM THIS

....

....

WOULD I DO IT AGAIN? ....

❧95❧

I WANT TO DO THIS BECAUSE

TO MAKE THIS HAPPEN I NEED

DATE COMPLETED

WHERE

SOLO – WITH

THE STORY

THE BEST PART

WHAT I LEARNED FROM THIS

WOULD I DO IT AGAIN?

∾96∾

I WANT TO DO THIS BECAUSE

TO MAKE THIS HAPPEN I NEED

DATE COMPLETED

WHERE

SOLO – WITH

THE STORY

THE BEST PART

WHAT I LEARNED FROM THIS

WOULD I DO IT AGAIN?

~97~

I WANT TO DO THIS BECAUSE

....

TO MAKE THIS HAPPEN I NEED

....

DATE COMPLETED ....

WHERE ....

SOLO – WITH ....

THE STORY

....

....

THE BEST PART

....

....

WHAT I LEARNED FROM THIS

....

....

WOULD I DO IT AGAIN? ....

~98~

I WANT TO DO THIS BECAUSE

....

TO MAKE THIS HAPPEN I NEED

....

DATE COMPLETED ....

WHERE ....

SOLO – WITH ....

THE STORY

....

....

THE BEST PART

....

....

WHAT I LEARNED FROM THIS

....

....

WOULD I DO IT AGAIN? ....

99

I WANT TO DO THIS BECAUSE

TO MAKE THIS HAPPEN I NEED

DATE COMPLETED

WHERE

SOLO – WITH

THE STORY

THE BEST PART

WHAT I LEARNED FROM THIS

WOULD I DO IT AGAIN?

✌ 100 ✌

....

I WANT TO DO THIS BECAUSE

....

TO MAKE THIS HAPPEN I NEED

....

DATE COMPLETED ....

WHERE ....

SOLO – WITH ....

THE STORY

....

....

THE BEST PART

....

....

WHAT I LEARNED FROM THIS

....

....

WOULD I DO IT AGAIN? ....

Printed in Great Britain
by Amazon

44693879R00066